# Brain I

# Our Hidden Journeys

To Calum,

Best Wishes,
Nathan

N Sacha
N.S,

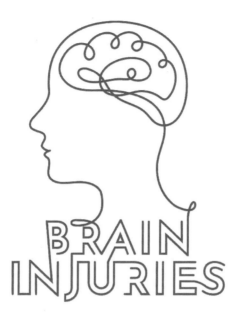

# BRAIN INJURIES

## OUR HIDDEN JOURNEYS

Nathan Shoesmith

Cover Art by Revo Creative Ltd
Publication Supported by Bay Buddies
Edition Dedicated to Amelia

Fraser House Hub
White Cross Business Park
South Road
Lancaster
Lancashire
LA1 4XQ

First Printed in Great Britain by Mixam
ISBN 978-1-3999-2472-6

To all those impacted by the pain and
confusion of brain injuries

# CONTENTS

**1**

# INTRODUCTION

*They say that you should never judge a
book by its cover, and in some ways, that
is what this book is all about.*

Human life is least to say, complex.
While we share some common
characteristics that make us living beings
and we often share similar traits that
bring groups of us together, we are all
unique in our ways.

On the outside, many of us look broadly
similar. If you happen to see a stranger
and acknowledge them as you are
walking along, you will probably
automatically notice things about them –
maybe their height, what they're wearing
or other seemingly insignificant facts.
Say you then see this person more
regularly, maybe every few days. Over
time, you begin to know about their
fashion choices, when they tend to
exercise, maybe if they have a pet – and

from this, it's possible that you may consciously or subconsciously start to judge and form an opinion around them.

You should not though judge a book, nor a person, by its cover.

While to a significant extent we may be able to identify facts or at least perceptions about people just from looking at them, we cannot see what is under the surface. Often, even talking to people is not enough, with many of us not letting on anywhere near as much as what is actually going on in our lives.

This book contains stories from real people whose lives have changed, in many cases quite dramatically. Some of these people struggle to carry out daily tasks that many of us may see as basic. Yet, if most of them walked past you in the street, you wouldn't realise it.

It is very easy to dislike a book cover and not read the book.

It is very easy to have one negative conversation with a stranger and never talk to them again.

It is very easy to look at or even talk to a person, know they have no broken bones and think they're 'okay', 'fine', or 'normal'.

It is easy to judge things at face value, but doing so is often to neglect attention to large parts of a story.

Hundreds, thousands and millions of us will at any one time be living through a hidden battle. These battles could be of any size, and they could happen to anyone. They could be about work, relationships, fighting a largely or wholly invisible disease, our mental health or a whole range of other topics. This book focuses on a particular type of hidden battle, arguably more misunderstood than most. A type of hidden disability which, for those that survive it, often see their lives and their outlooks on them changed monumentally.

That hidden disability is acquired brain injury.

In 2016/17, there was approximately one acquired brain injury admission to UK hospitals every 90 seconds. Brain injuries, and particularly the effects of them, are often misunderstood and them often not being visible to the naked eye can be partially attributed to this.

This book contains real life stories of people who have faced an acquired brain injury – how the injuries happened, their effects, and what has happened to their lives since. In some ways the stories in this book can be upsetting, and not the easiest to take in. In other ways though, these stories are important stories of massive strength, inspiring resilience and hope shining through.

This book aims to give a voice to the people whose stories it contains, many of whom may not have otherwise had the chance to speak up. It is also hugely important to help raise vital awareness of brain injuries - first published on Action for Brain Injury Week, this book aims to improve public understanding, and will raise vital funds to support survivors of brain injuries present and future.

The stories of facing and recovering from brain injuries, both from patients and carers are rarely easy, but they do need to be told and understood.

**2**

# ABOUT THIS BOOK

The stories from this book have been written in the words of those whose stories they are. Brain injuries affect different people in different ways, meaning that for some people, how much of their story they can remember and how well they can communicate is impacted by their injury. As such, the stories were curated in different ways – some by interviews, some by conversations with family members, and some drafted directly by those who were injured – edited into sentences, approved for sharing and brought together in this publication. These stories are based on the recollections of those who experienced them and have not been adapted for dramatic or other effect.

Telling a story of personal challenges can require great courage and strength. Some of the people who shared their stories are vulnerable individuals. In order to protect the identities of those who have shared their stories, random names have been attributed to some of the stories in the main part of this book.

This book aims to bring together insights about the impacts of brain injuries on the basis of detailed conversations and interviews with a variety of people to have been impacted by acquired brain injury, and some personal experiences. These insights are brought together through a series of thematic intros and individual stories. The stories in this book are included in chapters based on themes, though each story can relate to many different themes and provide a variety of insights.

This book does not aim to give medical advice and has been written by those to experience the contained stories, rather than clinicians or other medical professionals. Brain injuries and their impacts can vary significantly – this book should not be used in the place of professional advice. A range of links to support will be provided towards the end of the book for anybody interested in seeking support.

The stories in this book are primarily from people currently based and supported by groups in the North West of England, though many of the stories were set in the past elsewhere. The stories discuss injuries that have happened in different parts of Great Britain and to people of a variety of ages, and in some cases how they have been supported since. While this book cannot cover all of the different themes around acquired brain injuries, it is hoped it will provide some insights into the lives of those with an ABI, and show that anyone, no matter their age or location, could be impacted.

ABI refers to acquired brain injury, which is any brain injury that has occurred since birth. There are many different types of brain injuries, causes and effects. Some, but not all of the types of brain injury include traumatic brain injuries such as penetrative or closed head injuries and concussion, strokes or brain tumours.

# 3

# OUT OF NOWHERE

*Lives can change in an instant.*

For some, the unpredictability of not knowing what is around the corner can be challenging and difficult to handle. For others, not knowing what comes next is exciting and stops life from being boring.

Either way, it is a fact in life that we cannot reasonably foresee everything that will happen in the future. We can spend time and energy trying to influence the future of ourselves and others, and usually most events can be attributed to a chain of events that have taken place previous to them.

Sometimes we may be able to piece together this chain of events, like as part of some type of accident investigation. However, a chain of events may be unknown to us and so out of our control as it develops into resulting situations.

Whether or not we should see them coming and whether they are reasonably avoidable or not, events in life can just seem to come to out of nowhere. Those events could be positive, but of course they could also be negative – sometimes life changing.

This chapter recalls the stories of some survivors who have had their lives changed in an instant through a brain injury, from road traffic collisions to simple trips and falls.

--

It can sometimes seem quite incredible how quickly things can happen, and often for worse than for better. Brain injury survivors will tell you that the process of being injured is often quick – the recovery can be anything but.

Where brain injuries are concerned, there are reasons for this – one being the fragility of the human brain. The brain is arguably the most important organ in the human body, with it controlling our actions, feelings and so much more. The brain has some protection – the exact specifics of which won't be touched upon in this book – but damaging that protection could cause problems.

If you break your arm, it will probably hurt, but chances are it's unlikely to do you any serious damage in the long run. If you have an impact injury or break bones in and around your head, it has the potential to be much worse.

It is true that one punch can kill a person.

It is a fact that most of us don't think about and one that can seem difficult to believe. It is though true, and while statistics on one punch deaths are limited, the potential impact of one punch is not to be underestimated.

A campaign was setup in the UK to raise awareness of how one punch can kill and aims to educate young people about the dangers of losing control of their temper. A quick search online will display some tragic reads of people who were knocked down and died within hours of suffering a brain injury. It is hugely important that awareness is built up about the dangers of any such fight, which are often misunderstood. The fact that one punch can kill shows the fragility of the head and brain.

For those that survive a blow to the head, the impacts can still be truly life changing. This is true not just for suffering punches or otherwise being injured in a fight, but in a whole range of situations, from sports accidents to car crashes, falls and freak accidents. Violence can arguably increase the likelihood of life-changing injury, but it is often the small things that we don't see coming or just seem so unlikely that we don't give them more than a moment's thought.

--

While it can be unpredictable events or accidents that can change lives, it doesn't always take a tangible event. We simply don't know what is happening in our bodies all of the time, meaning health conditions can develop over time and if asymptomatic, may go undetected. As well as those that have received a sudden injury, some of the stories in this chapter are from people who have only noticed something is not right upon experiencing sudden illness. The thought of some hidden disease developing inside of you can be scary and prompt a significant amount of anxiety, as some stories in this book explain.

Whatever happens, and why it happens, in life we don't always know what is around the corner.

Lives really can change in an instant.

# William

### 39 - London, 2005

*I would get another bike in an instant, if only I could mount one.*

I was driving alone the south circular road in London when it happened. It was busy, had just started to rain but I hadn't been speeding. In the accident, I went over the top of a Range Rover as it pulled out of a side turning – the driver of which later apologised.

Following the accident, I was admitted to hospital in Leatherhead. My skull wasn't broken and at the time, I had been wearing a helmet. Between my time in Leatherhead and another rehab hospital in Putney, I spent around 8 years rehabilitating from the accident.

Before the accident, I had a car as well as my bike and was a car trader and stockbroker. I preferred my job buying and selling cars. I used to play a guitar, but now, my hands can't work properly. In hospital it was found that my middle fingers don't work properly, and I was given a pin in my left knee – the accident also leaving a scar down the front of my left shin.

I was discharged from hospital in 2013 and married my sweetheart on my birthday just months later. My wife, and the rest of my family had stayed by me and supported me lots during my time in rehab. In the same year, I moved to be closer to my family. My wife, the love of my life, acted as my carer until she passed away with cancer at the age of 61.

I now have a new carer that visits me twice a day and does shopping for me, but I can do a lot for myself and have had disability facilities installed at my home. I still struggle walking somewhat and get tired quickly, though do what I can. In the future, I'd like to be able to drive again.

I walk around the block 9 times a day and am a big fan of sports. I support Tottenham Hotspur and am a big fan of Formula 1 and MotoGP.

Being part of a Headway group has meant I always have someone to talk to. They are all a great bunch of people and very supportive.

I believe my story is important to share. At points there wasn't much hope, but my family stayed by me and I have come a very long way from where I was after my accident.

# Austin

**55 - Cheshire, 2017**

*When I got up, I knew something wasn't right.*

I woke up at 05.30am for work and walked to my bathroom. As I did, I knew something wasn't right. I couldn't communicate and couldn't go to the phone. I laid down on the bathroom floor.

At the time, I was self-employed and didn't live with my partner. I was working in construction and had been under stress in my job. I was found in my home 15 hours later. My partner realised something was wrong when she didn't hear from me. When coming to my house, she saw my curtains hadn't been opened that day and she raised the alarm. When she found me, I couldn't speak, but could manage some facial movement.

I was rushed straight to Macclesfield A&E, then Stoke once it was discovered I had suffered a stroke. I had a craniotomy to stop the brain swelling, which ultimately saved my life.

I spent two weeks in an Intensive Care Unit. I was in a bad way – I couldn't breathe on my own and had a tracheostomy to support my breathing.

My family was told I would be looking at life in a wheelchair. The stroke had damaged the communication and language parts of my brain, meaning I don't always understand what people say to me. I still have my intelligence from before, but I can't communicate.

After leaving intensive care, I was moved onto an acute medical ward. I was in hospital for around 7 months before being sent home. I had both family and carers going in to support me but couldn't cope at first. For a further 6 months, I had to spend time in a rehabilitation unit. Following the stroke, I spent a total of 12 months on a feeding tube.

During the time I spent in rehab, I started to be able to eat, make a drink, shower and dress myself. Despite fears that I would be limited to using a wheelchair for the rest of my life, I can now walk around by myself.

After leaving rehab, I moved closer to my family who support me each week. I can use my coordination and have a good sense of humour, though am limited in my communication skills.

# Jessica

**53 - Lancashire, 2014**

*The doctors were preparing to transplant organs to other patients when my eye opened.*

I had just learnt to drive and was a fully qualified chef. I was at home and had been drinking a bit when the accident happened. While going to the toilet, I had a fall and fell down the stairs.

At the time and for some time after the accident I didn't understand what had actually happened. I later found out some parts of the story, including my daughter shouting at me to wake up, and my son in law performing CPR while waiting for an ambulance to arrive.

I was in hospital for 13 months, though remember very little about the time I spent there, being in a coma at first. One point that does stand out in my memory was how nice the nurses were that looked after me.

I reached the point where the hospital staff were switching off machines ready for my body to die. The doctors were preparing to transplant my organs to other patients, though they didn't reach that point. Before they could do so and while my family were saying goodbye, one of my eyes opened, understandably scaring them all.

I couldn't talk or do very much in hospital. Eventually, I managed to start walking and regained my ability to communicate, being discharged after 13 months. After leaving hospital, I went to live with my daughter. I couldn't remember the house; I couldn't walk upstairs and things I'm told don't always sink in.

Today, I can walk some distance but find it hard to walk too far. I have had epilepsy since the injury and have been trying to get used to different tablets to treat this, with my daughter supporting me as my carer.

Looking back now, I think I was lucky.

A nurse that came to my house told me about Headway and at first, I wasn't too bothered, but thought I'd have a go at visiting the local group. I asked my parents to come with me and at the group. I felt like crying because of how nice and friendly the people were. I immediately made new friends despite not knowing anyone and feel part of the 'family'.

You often don't realise that people have got head or brain injuries. Being able to meet and spend time with other people who have experienced similar injuries gives you strength, so I think the work of volunteers is exceptional.

# Sophie

**31 - Bury, 1988**

*For all life's ups and downs, to wake up
in a morning and live is a wonderful gift.*

I was in my early 30s out shopping in
Bury market when it happened. I
collapsed in the street and was rushed to
hospital, told that I had a brain
hemorrhage.

I was in hospital for about 3 months, and
during this time I developed a lump in
my right calf. The lump turned out to be
a blood clot and I was put on warfarin. I
had to stay in another couple of weeks
before I was then discharged.

When I was discharged, I came out in a
wheelchair. I could not walk or speak. I
was informed by my employer that they
could not keep me with them because of
my condition. I loved my job and was
devastated. I could not speak, walk, talk
and I had lost my job. I felt useless, lost
and without a future. I cannot describe
the absolute hopelessness I felt and this

sent me into bouts of depression that would last for days and cause me not to want to see anyone.

My husband took me to a specialist and I tried tablets for depression. I was up and down for a long time and my right side was affected by my condition, including my face, arm, leg and also my speech. My husband helped me about, helped with daily tasks I struggled to complete, drove me about and had to work extra hours.

We had almost got my depression under control after many weeks. I got to walking with a stick, but tripped up and fell a lot. I fell and broke my good arm and it was in plaster for weeks – another setback. Having two useless arms instead of just one gave me more feelings of uselessness and I had more treatment for depression. I also had a full knee replacement and more physio to help me walk again.

My husband had time off work and concentrated on my walking with a stick and helped my speech come back on. I have since had another thrombosis in my right leg, leading to another spell in hospital. I am currently waiting for an operation to straighten my right foot and I need a knee replacement but don't know when it will happen.

Like many people I was unlucky, but I survived so I am very lucky.

When I joined Headway, I met some lovely people who have helped me get back to normal and I am very thankful to them all.

# Lionel

### Thailand, 2019

*My work permit was revoked – I had to return to England.*

I was working in Thailand as an English Teacher in 2019 when I suffered a major stroke. The stroke left me with many disabilities and I spent 2 months in a rehabilitation centre before returning home to my partner and 2-year-old daughter.

My disabilities meant that I was unable to return to work. I had paralysis of my right side, incontinence, dysphasia and aphasia – in turn this meant that my work permit was revoked and I could no longer remain in Thailand.

In February 2020 I had to return to England, leaving behind my partner and daughter. A short time after my return, we entered the first lockdown because of the coronavirus pandemic. This led to my rehabilitation being fragmented. Initially I had been offered physiotherapy, occupational therapy and input from the speech and language department. However, due to coronavirus the sessions from these departments were halted at different times which made it difficult for me to make any real progress.

The Stroke Association were of a great help on my return to the UK, but again because of COVID and the lockdown that was imposed, any groups that were offered had to be stopped. The association's website offered invaluable information for both me and my Mum, though I was unable to read myself.

At the time I was feeling socially isolated. I had not only had to leave my friends and family behind in Thailand where I had lived for 15 years; I had to come and live where I didn't have any friends. This was made more difficult by the continuing lockdown.

6 months after returning to England I was able to move into my own flat with input from my Mum and care agencies. Although I wanted to be independent, I found it difficult to carry out tasks that many people take for granted. I sometimes became very frustrated and angry.

I become particularly frustrated when people can't understand what I am trying to say because of communication problems. I had to try and manage my aggression and others had to try and learn how to cope with it. I have heard obsessive compulsive disorder is common to develop after a stroke and having some structure and routine has helped me improve and be more independent.

I still have many physical and mental impairments though my speech has improved over time. However, I often get 'yes' and 'no' mixed up which causes frustration when people don't understand what I actually mean. Using thumbs up and thumbs down can help.

I can understand everything that is spoken to me but what I try to write does not always make sense. I am also very limited to how much I can read and can usually only make sense of very short sentences. Writing is also now much more difficult since my brain injury. I can walk unaided albeit very slowly.

Upon joining the local Headway group, I was able to join a gym which I now attend regularly. This helps me from a physical, psychological and social point of view and I am more interactive through meeting other people I can identify with.

I am mainly now continent with only the occasional accident. I lost the use of my right arm following my stroke which makes some normal tasks difficult, such as being able to fasten shoelaces or zips on a coat. Many different gadgets have though helped me become as independent as possible.

Before my stroke I used to drive but have had to surrender my driving license and now depend on over people taking me out. Over recent months I have accepted my situation more but am sometimes reluctant to mix with others.

I enjoy visiting the gym on a regular basis, have lunch out once a week and enjoy watching sport on television – specifically Liverpool Football Club.

**4**

# FACING THE CHALLENGES OF ABI

*Why me?*

Sustaining a brain injury can seem unfair, distressing and difficult to comprehend. At one point or another, many people that have received the diagnosis of a damaging health condition will have mentally asked themselves the question, 'why me?'

It can sometimes be difficult to do anything but ruminate over this question of 'why me?' Thinking about it isn't going to change what has happened, but it is often a natural reaction to try and understand the causes of an injury.

Unfortunately, many brain injuries cannot be seen coming, and they could happen to absolutely anyone. Young or old, healthy or unhealthy – there may be risk factors, but brain injuries can affect anyone, which can make trying to understand them particularly difficult.

Brain injuries can sometimes only be partially diagnosed, and the extent and periods of recovery can be incredibly difficult to predict. Not knowing what the future may hold can be exciting, but this is unlikely to be the case so much while trying to recover from an injury.

A traumatic injury can cause a significant amount of anxiety for some survivors, and the stories in this chapter provide some insights into this. This could be anxiety about whether they will recover and how long this may take, or maybe about whether they are able to perform their existing responsibilities and achieve goals they may have set out. In recent times as more work has been done to tackle the stigma around mental health, some people have started to talk more openly about and recognise anxiety related to health – health anxiety. For those that have received a distressing health diagnosis or have had a major injury, they may become anxious and start to question their health more and more whenever something doesn't seem quite right. These feelings can be added to by instances of difficulty in accessing medical support, or facing long wait times in order to do so. Some people may stay away from some situations for fear of picking up an injury, illness or disease – parallels can be drawn here to the feelings many reported during or after coronavirus lockdowns.

In addition to health anxiety, the impacts of brain injuries can see some worried about whether they will be able to fulfil their commitments, look after others or pay the bills. Even for those that receive support, these tasks can often be daunting, especially if they are the ones responsible for sourcing and funding any such support or have not been made aware of services which may be able to help.

Brain injuries can also have a major impact on friendships, relationships and family interactions. While some friends, family and partners can be incredibly supportive and while some injuries can grow the bond between people, many relationships can unfortunately fall apart or be damaged after a brain injury. It is known that the impacts of brain injuries can make a range of romantic and sexual activities difficult, while interactions with others can also be significantly affected by communication, coordination, cognitive or other challenges.

The brain is arguably the most important organ in the human body, and injuries to it are arguably more impactful and difficult to work through than many other possible injuries. Recovery from a brain injury can often mean much more than waiting for a bone to heal or some swelling to go down, but working to understand and learning to live with a range of other impacts.

The questions of 'why me' and searching for answers in pursuit of recovery can be confusing and hugely challenging. These challenges may often not be recognised by others and may even be dismissed by some – the true stories in this chapter can help to give further insight into recovery from a brain injury.

# Jane

**48 - Lancashire, 2019**

*I was told I would of died if I hadn't of got to hospital.*

I was admitted to hospital after I had become very ill, my temperature reaching 42.2°C. I was unconscious for 12 hours before I woke up.

While in hospital, it took some time to stabilise me to the point that I could be discharged – about a month in fact. During my time in hospital, I had many different tests before I was then diagnosed with a brain tumour.

To date, I have had 6 scans and I am waiting to hear some results. Currently it is just being monitored – I have been told it may not get any bigger but it is not fully understood.

Sometimes I experience memory loss and dizziness. I wonder whether this is related to the tumour as none of this happened before my illness. I experience some anxiety and wonder if there is something I am not being told. I call it 'ticky tocky' – I don't know how I will be in years to come.

By chance I met other people with brain injuries and this community has helped me to keep my sanity together. I felt I needed something new in my life and many people I know have been cautious to come out after lockdown.

I struggled with health anxiety during the coronavirus pandemic, as well as sometimes thinking about my head. On one occasion I had to use public transport during the lockdowns to have my tumour scanned. I had a very bad experience and suffered significant anxiety through the travelling.

As well as working through my own challenge, I am a carer for my husband and brother as required, while providing support to multiple other family members.

I feel there needs to be much more advice out there about brain injuries, and also much more awareness. The support I have been given by talking about my tumour with others is amazing and has helped me put my thoughts together to try and get through it.

# Clara

**48 - Blackpool, 2013**

*I know the angels were looking down on me.*

I was cycling on a Sunday evening in the summer when a violent thunderstorm broke out. I was coming down a hill on my bicycle with no helmet. As I turned a corner, I slipped on a drain, hit the curb and somersaulted off my bicycle. I smacked the back of my head and lay unconscious on a very busy road.

Two people were driving behind me and saw the accident unfold. Those two people were paramedics, so I know the angels were looking down on me. The paramedics stopped the traffic in both directions, which I later heard had backed up for 5 miles in each direction. An ambulance was called for and I was taken to A&E, completely unaware of what was happening as I remained unconscious for 4 hours.

I woke up in hospital freezing cold about midnight. I had blood on my pillow but couldn't lift my head off the pillow. Stretched out on a bed in A&E, I asked if I could get a blanket as I was shaking. I was transferred to a ward and woke up the next morning with the type of incredible headache that I had never known before. I could feel it in the core, centre of my brain, all over my head, with pain also reaching down my neck, back and right down to my feet. I was in agony. Painkillers were provided, but they didn't seem to make any difference.

I was discharged just a day after my accident and picked up by my daughter. My skull had been fractured but put back together. At the time I had been my Mum's main carer and so I wanted to get back and see her – I probably wouldn't of wanted to stay around in hospital any longer than I did.

The day after discharge I returned to the hospital to ask for different painkillers due to being in agonising pain. I was then told exactly what had happened in the accident and its impacts. I had wrenched muscles at the base of my neck, the brain had gone forward and was swelling due to the wrenching movement of the accident. I also had a bone hairline fracture with severed nasal strands that affected my sense of smell going to the brain.

Over the next 6 months following my discharge, I continued to experience severe headaches. I had been feeling like I had been spinning on a merry go round and my balance was affected.

I was taken for an MRI scan which just confirmed everything that had been said previously. I had been needing more sleep and was being woken up by my Mum who had dementia and kept trying to wake me up.

12 months after the accident I had a CT scan on my fractured skull and was then advised not to go away on a holiday which I had booked to include scuba

diving. During the year I had kept going to my doctor with throbbing pain and this continued for years to come.

About 5 years after the accident I tried to enrol on a college course to try to improve my situation. One of the lecturers recognised that I wouldn't be able to complete the course and recommended a local group.

The group has been very supportive and has allowed me to make new friends. I helped some of the other members enjoy swimming, as a swimming teacher myself. I love going swimming with others and trying to get fit again, though I have to be careful. I went for a swim in 2016 and pushed myself, ploughing up and down the pool. When I got out of the pool I couldn't walk straight and just needed to sit down. For half an hour I thought I wouldn't be able to get off the bench I was sitting on and I vomited. It was a scary feeling and I think I over-exerted myself. I eventually drove home though was petrified and worried about what had happened. I have always done swimming and raced against European champions when I was a teenager, but now realised I have to pace myself.

In recent times, I have managed to do my lifeguarding certificates and work in large indoor waterparks.

Meeting other people that have experienced similar injuries has really opened my eyes to realise how lucky I am. I've met so many people who are worse off than me.

I am a big football supporter and love following the game. I have a very strong support network and compassionate friends. I don't want to be seen as incapable, I want to be strong and confident and want to learn how to say no to things I can no longer manage.

I try not to get frustrated, accept my situation for what it is, and to do my best.

# Colin

**18 - Somerset, 1999**

*I started to get anxious and felt like something wasn't right.*

My friend asked me if I wanted to go with their group in order to pick up a car, and to take it somewhere for delivery.

The car was a BMW M3 and I thought why not, it would be a laugh.

One of my friend's parents, who was also involved, drove us to the location where we were going to pick up the BMW – a set of garages/lock-ups. On arrival, two of us including myself stayed in the car, while my friends got out and told me to wait.

Outside it was dark and as I looked to my right, I could see in the moonlight what appeared to be people in the bushes. At this point I started to get anxious and felt like something wasn't right and something bad was going to happen to me.

The driver, who was still in the car with me, received a text message – I could hear the 'buzz buzz' of the message arriving. The message was an instruction for me to get out of the car and to walk around the corner of the lockups. It was dark, we were out on the Moors and I didn't know where I was – I felt like I couldn't turn back and so followed the instructions.

As I turned the corner, I could see a person with dark hair who then disappeared into a lock-up. I also proceeded to walk to the lock-up where I then met with my friends before walking inside. Once inside, we walked up some stairs and could see a number of cars – a green BMW, a white BMW and a kid car on a ramp. At the top of the stairs, my friends said we had to find the keys for the BMW and I was told to check a set of the drawers.

I felt very dubious, as if I was being setup, but I also felt like I would be screwed over if I didn't do what they said.

Once finished upstairs, we went down to the cars. My friends told me to go over to the gate, pick up a scaffolding bar and hold it above my head, against the lock.

I was knocked out.

I eventually woke up in hospital, unable to move and unable to talk. I later learned that I had spent 3 weeks and 6 days in a coma.

My family, who had been visiting me in hospital, had tried to prove to doctors that I could understand what they were saying. I was paralysed and couldn't interact with them, but my eyeballs followed conversations, my brain understanding them. In order to try and provoke a reaction, they told me that my sound system had been broken. When told this, my body started shaking violently. I took some time to calm down.

As time went on, I began to be able to use a spell board to write what had happened on the evening of the accident, though I greatly struggled to coordinate properly. At this time, I was told that my friends had an accident and had died, though many years on I believe I have seen them in public.

My accident at 18 years old has majorly changed my life. I got married after the accident but struggled to have an emotional relationship – being unable to cry since the accident. I made mistakes again and again in my relationship, and it ended, with our daughter taken away from me.

Today, I struggle with my balance, I struggle with eating, drinking and swallowing, and I usually get pneumonia yearly.

Nearly a decade ago, I started seeing Headway on the back of advice from my solicitor. Headway were helpful in helping me to get the right benefits, as my benefits had been stopped when I left residential rehab for my brain injury. I regularly visit the local Headway group.

While not everybody liked me due to my nationality, I used to be a charmable, likeable person. Now, most people wouldn't know there is something wrong with me, but there is.

I feel unhappy, unable to be in a relationship, and lonely.

# Lisa

### 14 - Renfrewshire, 1975

*I felt like I was left for dead.*

At a young age I was attacked with a poker and suffered some broken bones which I was treated for in an A&E unit.

Many years later, I had my ribs broken, arms and legs bruised and was left with internal bleeding in an attack. I felt like I had been 'left for dead'. At the time, the hospital scanned every part of my body, except from my head.

Over the next 2 years, I presented to numerous doctors multiple times. I was told I had depression, but anti-depressants didn't seem to help me.

Eventually, I was given an MRI scan, which identified two brain damages. It is believed that I had a stroke previously during an attack that wasn't identified at the time.

I was sent to memory clinics where I was told that I had a memory problem. It was described to me that I have a memory box which records memories when I do things, but I just don't have a library card.

I was told that there was no specific support I could receive for this condition. I have since had to get carers, but it is down to me to pay them, sort out insurance for them and complete other paperwork. I find this particularly difficult given my memory problem.

I started seeing the local Headway group in 2020 and they were a massive help. The volunteers were able to help with completing forms and becoming part of the community. I've gained more confidence from coming to the groups and I find the groups to be more understanding than some other people.

It is really valuable to know there is someone there just the other side of a phone call.

# 5

# CHANGING THE OUTLOOK

*Quite often, you don't realise quite how much things mean to you until you no longer have them.*

Given the events of recent years, the above statement may resonate with more people than before.

The series of lockdowns experienced throughout the world from 2020 in response to the COVID-19 coronavirus pandemic fundamentally changed the way we all lived. For months at a time, we were separated from friends, families and loved ones. Strict restrictions meant that for a time, we lost the freedoms to live our lives how we wanted – being ordered to stay at home, work from home and then severely limit our in-person contact with others. Tragically, many people lost loved ones more permanently to the virus, some not even getting to say goodbye.

The coronavirus pandemic saw us lose things that we often just take for granted. Whether that's being able to meet up with friends after work, or even being able to go to work through a commute longer than walking from your bedroom to your kitchen. With it being easy to take many things for granted, we often don't appreciate our ability to do them there in that moment - rather we only think about them when they are no longer there.

At the time of publication, COVID-19 is still very much present in most of the world, though for the most part in the UK, restrictions on our daily lives in response to the virus have all but ceased. For some, there has been a desire to get back to how we used to do things before the pandemic, though the way in which the world has changed means that this is no longer practical, efficient or results in the same effect. From travel routines, to patterns and locations of work, how we spend time with people and much else about our lives has changed. Some more than others have embraced this, and taken a mindset of appreciating regained freedoms much more than when we often took them for granted.

The story of the coronavirus pandemic is continuing to be written, but with what has already happened in recent years, its impacts are in some ways a metaphor for the life-changing scenarios faced by those who live through traumatic injuries and health conditions, including brain injuries.

--

The survivors of brain injuries can have to work through some incredibly tough times before they can even start to think about living aspects of a 'normal' life. For some, life post-brain injury may be severely limited forever – others will be more fortunate. Every person is unique and no two brain injuries and their impacts will be quite the same – making treatment and recovery hard to predict.

For those fortunate to survive and make a significant recovery from a brain injury, the experience can shift one's outlook on life, and also those around them. Going through a traumatic injury or health condition can be quite a scare and provoke feelings like those we touched upon earlier where you only fully appreciate the value in things when they are gone – or at real risk of going away.

For brain injury survivors, the change in outlook can manifest itself in different ways. Some of which were noted in conversations during the collation of this book include;

- Re-evaluating relationships

- Moving closer to the people you care about

- Noticing and expressing much more the appreciation for the simple things, such as a call with a friend or a walk in the rain

- Reconsidering career choices and what is important to you

- Looking to make the most of everyday

- Increased desire to explore and fulfil items from a bucket list

- Becoming closer than ever with friends and family

- Cutting out bad habits and changing your philosophy

- Much less tendency to complain

- Using periods of recovery as time to reflect and to search for ways to lead a happier life

Exactly how trauma can sometimes lead to positives for those who have sustained them is difficult to describe, but it is sometimes true. While none of us want to experience trauma in the first place, the eventual recovery from them can bring some positives, even if they are usually hard to find.

Unfortunately, though, as this book has already explored, recovery sometimes does not come, and where it does, any positives may be limited. The following stories in this chapter can though provide some hope that for many people, things can and will get better.

Through our daily lives, most of us will at some stage moan or complain about something, sometimes within reason and sometimes more trivially.

We often don't realise quite how much things mean to us until we lose them. As touched upon already, lives can be changed in an instant, so for those that have had their lives changed, there is often the tendency to make the most of everyday and take much less for granted.

For those that face trauma, they can lose so much – often through no fault of our own, it can sometimes be difficult to truly appreciate how lucky we are just to experience the basics and live a 'normal' life.

# Catherine

## Lancashire, 2012

*The stroke completely changed my life.*

It was in 2012 that I suddenly collapsed at home, without any warning. My daughter was near me at the time and upon finding me lying unconscious on the floor, quickly called for an ambulance. I was rushed to hospital and placed in a coma.

I stayed in multiple hospitals and trauma centres and spent half of the year that followed drifting in and out of consciousness, feeling in a confused state. I had suffered a stroke and was given a 50% chance of survival.

I was paralysed down my right-hand side and had developed aphasia, meaning I have some communication difficulties. The first months after the stroke were the most frightening of my life – I was in shock and felt very vulnerable.

I was overjoyed once I was able to leave hospital, but my life has changed and is very different to how it used to be. I used to be a teacher and NHS manager, and for a while thought I may not be able to do any of my hobbies again.

Today, I am very dependent of my friends and family and I have been on a long journey of recovering to try to get my life back on track. My hard work completing different exercises from physio and speech experts has paid off and I've seen myself improve over time.

Through Headway, I have met lots of new friends and I feel like they are understanding to what I have been going through. I've got to be part of inspiring and wonderful experiences including outdoor holidays for disabled people. Without Headway, the NHS, my family, friends, faith and community, I wouldn't have been able to do what I can now.

I am now able to enjoy swimming, walking, gardening, rock wall climbing, hiking, shopping and other activities. I need help for some of those, but can do more than I used to be able to and I am very grateful to those dedicated people that offer their support to me.

Some people have responded really positively to my disability and have been very supportive, though some have responded more negatively and I have had to face this as a challenge.

I have come a long way and now want to use my experience of having experienced a brain injury in order to help others.

# Gary

*I faced up to 10 years of memory loss and vagueness, and I could only recall other people's installed memories to my recollection of the time up until starting rehabilitation.*

I was admitted to hospital where my Glasgow Coma Scale was assessed as level 3. My Frontal Lobe, Occipital Lobe and Pituitary Gland were all damaged in my head. This led to me being placed in an induced coma for four weeks.

I had one wrist which was held together by a metal plate because of how badly it was broken. I also broke bones on the other side of my body, but because they were not plated straight away, the bones started to repair themselves incorrectly. This left my arm being unable to rotate properly due to the infusion of the bones. My pituitary gland had also been affected leading to me needing primarily growth hormones and testosterone, though this has since fortunately reduced to just growth hormones.

The only smell and tastes I have now is wood and metal. I lost the sensation of hunger and thirst, and was threatened with sectioning unless I did eat and drink. As soon as something reaches the back of my mouth, I am unable to sense this in my body. My windpipe doesn't always close, which can lead to me occasionally choking. Swallowing can also sometimes be a problem due to the muscles/nerves not always functioning correctly. My bowels and bladder do not always alert me to the need to empty them, which leads to me ending up in crippling pain owing to them being over full. These are just some of the nerves and muscles which do not work properly anymore.

My internal temperature gauge only sometimes works correctly. Once, I sat outside for 3 hours while the temperature was -6°C as my body told me it was warm enough to be outside.

While I was slowly on the mend, I was moved around different wards that had space in them, and eventually I was moved to my local hospital. This hospital had not been made aware of my brain injury – this led to me being seen a mile away by a former work friend, whom notified the police that I was in my hospital pyjamas walking home and would not get in his car to return me to hospital. Once I was seen fit enough, I was placed in the hospital rehabilitation centre.

I eventually returned home. I was fearful every time I went for a walk as I had been told I might not be able to control my temper and potentially become violent.

This never occurred but this fear had been instilled into me.

I became part of the over 80% of relationships that do not survive following such an injury and I lost all of my friends except from 2. To retain my driving license, I had to do a disabled driver assessment, which I passed without a problem.

At first, I was expected to be bed bound for life if I even survived, but I managed to undergo significant recovery and the consultants I was under discharged me. I have since done seven years of education enabling me to attend university, though unfortunately had to finish this to support my daughter through a rare cancer.

I have again chosen to return to university, to get qualified in a medical field to be able to give to others the help I received in a time of need.

Finally, I have found someone who has captured my heart, and have been able to have a beautiful, amazing and wonderful child. My one wish and desire are that we, together, become an exceptional family.

I had no involvement in the cause of my accident and do not want to become again a statistic of survivors who get an acquired brain injury.

# Tim

**31 - Norwich, 2019**

*Last week I celebrated the 3-year anniversary of my head injury.*

I know the term 'celebrated' might sound odd, however, ever since I suffered a mild brain trauma, I have been determined to take more from the injury than it has taken from me.

The injury occurred back in March 2019 whilst playing hockey. I sustained a blow to the head via a deflected ball. After feeling nauseous for a few hours, I returned back to the club to socialise and then went to work as normal for two days. On the fourth day after injury, I suffered the first of what would be countless 'crashes'. These were completely debilitating fatigue crashes that would leave me bed ridden for hours and sometimes days. Along with tinnitus, headaches, light sensitivity, noise sensitivity and dizziness, my brain shut down and let me perform only the most remedial tasks. Cooking was a struggle, walking to the end of the road impossible and holding a conversation exhausting. My mental health plummeted. I soon realised this was going to be a serious long-term recovery that would hugely impact my life. If someone at this point had said I would be 'celebrating' a head injury anniversary, I would have considered them mad.

After three months my recovery significantly improved. I became intent on mapping my recovery and recording every detail. This really helped maintain a focus but my obsession for my recovery was holding back my acceptance of the injury. Having previously played hockey at a high level and more recently held a management post in a busy school, I was not accustomed to slowing down; being active was part of my identity. I realised I needed to open up and sought help from a physio and psychologist as well as reaching out to Facebook groups and podcasts. I remembered reading an account from a head injury sufferer who said they wanted to 'take more from the injury than it had taken from me'. I found this inspiring. It became my mantra.

Within the next year I slowly improved with peaks and troughs that exhausted me both physically and mentally. Spotting progress was hard and often I would return to previous walks or cycle old routes to remember how far I was progressing. With a loving and supportive wife who supported my every moment, I was also fortunate to have an empathetic employer and I managed to arrange a 9 month return to work plan which was central to my recovery. I also fully embraced the four P's: pacing, prioritising, planning and preparation and recognised that balance and pacing were essential to minimising crashes.

After a year I began cycling, undertaking longer walks and returned to social settings with high stimulus.

As the months and years passed, I started to realise the positive impacts of the injury. It presented a reset for my outlook on life. I became much more aware of disabilities and invisible illnesses and developed a greater empathy for longer term chronic illnesses which thousands of people suffer with every day. I slowed down and began to be more appreciative of my environment, my friendships and my life which was full of happiness and love.

As I've continued to improve, I have continued to hold these values close and reflect regularly on the positive aspects of life. These values, along with the four Ps have become central to my life post-injury and I know they have made me a better husband, father, friend and colleague. Although I still suffer with symptoms, this without doubt, is cause for celebration. I know I will take more from my brain injury than it has taken from me.

# Nathan

**19 - Lancashire, 2020**

*I was walking along a campus pavement, which would usually be busy, though for a short period, there was only myself and one other person on that particular stretch.*

As the person in front of me was walking, they seemed to stumble slightly, potentially as if they had been drinking. I remember the person's elbow hitting the top left of my forehead as I walked past them. I felt the impact and felt strange for a few seconds, though I was not knocked out. I remember looking back towards them, and it seemed like they hadn't even realised what had happened. Nobody had witnessed what had happened and neither did any CCTV cameras - it could or could not have been accidental.

I continued walking and my friends soon caught up. My head hurt a little bit, but I was able to go to bed later that night and not think that much about it.

The next day, I had a dull headache and felt a little disorientated. I went about my day as usual but was advised by the afternoon to visit A&E due to me not seeming myself and a small area of swelling now being visible where my head had been impacted. A quick trip to A&E saw me discharged with mild concussion and handed a generic leaflet on head injuries. I was told I should recover within 48 hours.

The following days were difficult, with multiple visits to the doctors and worsening symptoms. I increasingly struggled with pain in my head, with headaches now seeming present more of the time than not and they were not responding well to painkillers. I couldn't listen to music properly, cope with telephone static noise, focus on reading or do many of the things that I would usually take for granted. As well as these temporary inabilities and the physical pain, there were consequential feelings of frustration and anxiety that no doubt added to the difficulty of what I was experiencing.

Shortly after seeing a doctor on the Monday evening, I was back at A&E and told to expect a 4 hour wait. Approximately 20 minutes later, I was taken into a triage room, asked the day of the week and who the Prime Minister was, and then told I'd been booked in for emergency brain scans.

A couple of hours after the scans I was informed the scans hadn't picked up anything out of the ordinary. I was told I'd probably had a more major concussion than first thought, and to take a couple of weeks off contact sports, but that I should be fine within days. I left A&E with the same leaflet on head injuries that I'd be given 4 days earlier. The knowledge that a scan had picked up nothing wrong was reassuring, but while it may have lifted some stress and anxiety, it didn't lift the symptoms I was experiencing.

The weeks that followed my injury were a constant learning curve, trying to work out what I could do and what I couldn't. As time passed, the pain I had been experiencing no longer happened all the time, but instead I started to become aware of triggers that would cause the headaches and pains that had become so common. I found that I couldn't sit for long in some meeting rooms or lecture theatres, with the theme seeming to be that I was affected by the lighting. I could walk around perfectly fine, but if I did so in daylight I pretty quickly got a headache, and one that worsened with any hills or incline. When I tried to run and swim after some weeks of resting, I found I could not do so at any significant intensity for more than a couple of minutes before being overwhelmed with pain. My concentration levels were much lower than usual, and my mind didn't fully focus on a book for more than 10 minutes. Right from the day of injury and continuing well beyond it, I'd been needing an extra 2 hours sleep a night, and would regularly be fatigued.

I presented to doctors multiple times in the 2 months that followed my injury to try and get some medical advice on how best to recover. Frustratingly, very similar tests that I was given a day after the injury were repeated, and for a while I was told the symptoms should go away after a few days - even weeks after the injury. In March, I was advised to see an optician, not urgently, but as a precaution. Just days later, the UK was plunged into its first national lockdown of the coronavirus pandemic.

Whether the timing of lockdown helped or hindered my recovery, I'm not sure I'll ever really know. The pandemic saw work and university largely grind to a halt, which meant that I had to worry less about my brain being in a fit state to meet deadlines. However, in hindsight, while I didn't feel them at the time, the impacts of isolation may have slowed my recovery in other areas.

I tried to keep myself as occupied as possible during lockdown while also taking some form of a break. I've never been too good at doing nothing, and while I don't regret how I spent my time, looking back I probably did too much. When the pandemic hit, my news media startup gained even more traction, and I found it difficult to say no to experiences of being on national television multiple times a week questioning government ministers and health experts about

COVID-19. Reflecting on it now, it seems strange that I was able to do this given the previous months of pain, though at the same time as doing this, I was still working through multiple symptoms and significant challenges. For the first time, I also started to experience mental health challenges, likely driven by a combination of injury and lockdown. In some ways, being able to write helped me massively in getting through lockdown, and my ability to write quickly helped in times where my usable time was much more restricted.

In the summer of 2020, I finally got to see an optician, and by chance one who had also had a head injury. Her advice was perhaps the most useful thing I heard that year. We worked out that the injury had seen me become particularly light sensitive, and wearing glasses lenses designed to deflect blue light and take the sharpness off things helped me feel much less pain over the course of the Autumn. While I still couldn't run or do high intensity sport, I was able to walk again in daylight, without a headache, around 8 months on from injury.

In early 2021, 13 months on from injury I was able to run again for the first time without pain on low incline routes. Within months, I'd built up from a 5K through to a first ever half marathon. My concentration improved, and in February 2022 I co-authored my first book while studying at university. I still need much more sleep, I still have to be careful around high intensity sport, I remain light sensitive and I have been learning to pace myself and relax a lot more than before.

When it comes to head and brain injuries, I consider myself one of the lucky ones. Like many others I've since met who have had similar injuries, I've spent time grappling with questions like 'why me' and spending far too much time ruminating. Being unable to see on a scan what I've experienced and having very little idea on what is and isn't possible and how recovery might pan out has made recent years a constant learning curve, but an experience that while negative, has positively changed my outlook on life.

I've learned that working flat out all week isn't sensible or aiding my recovery. I've learnt that I need to plan much more what I do in order to avoid fatigue and pain, and that sometimes doing almost nothing is the best way to make progress. I have also though learnt much more about the value in the things that I can do, having had times of losing some of them, and having seen how quickly lives can change. A combination of injury, lockdown and hearing the stories of others less fortunate in their injuries has led me to aim to make the most out of every day and no longer tend to take the small things for granted.

# 6

# VOLUNTEERS & CARERS

*There are some people in life who will go above and beyond to support others.*

*These people will often sacrifice many aspects of their own lives in order to make someone else's life better.*

*These people offer to work through some of the most difficult circumstances, even if they are under no obligation to do so.*

*These people are family, friends, volunteers, healthcare professionals and carers – and they are truly inspirational.*

Carers are sadly often underappreciated, but they can have hugely positive impacts on people's lives that are not to be understated. This book has looked at some of the challenges faced by people who have acquired brain injuries, and while these struggles can be difficult enough, those that experience brain injuries are not the only ones to be impacted by them.

For many people, a brain injury can be life changing, and sadly this tends to be in negative ways. As some of the stories in this book have recalled, brain injuries can leave people with communication, mobility and other challenges that make the performance of some basic tasks incredibly difficult. Most of us take for granted the normally simple things like being able to get dressed in the morning and prepare food. For some brain injury survivors though, these things are far from simple, and they rely on others to help support their performance of them.

The system of getting carers in place for someone with an acquired brain injury can be challenging, but so can the process of caring for someone with that injury. Having a brain injury can be incredibly frustrating and the impacts of some injuries can also prompt anger or other habits which can make the jobs of carers even more challenging. Some carers are able to receive training on how best to look after those with acquired brain injuries, but for many the role of a carer is much more informal.

Many carers are simply friends, family, neighbours, volunteers or other community heroes that come to the aid of those that need them. Many people will offer help with no expectation of anything back, will regularly put others first, and work long hours on a voluntary basis to improve the lives of others. This is both true for those supporting people with acquired brain injuries, and also a range of other health conditions.

Stories in this book have recalled how friends and family have supported people day in, day out, to help them get around and live as full a life as possible. While many people will stand by those that have been through trauma, experiencing a brain injury can also lead to the end of both friendships and relationships. This makes the work of charities and support groups especially important, as they can create a supportive community where people can receive help and have someone to talk to.

Compiled independently of any charities, this book has noted some of the many charities and community organisations across the country which run support groups which provide incredible support and services to help improve life after brain injury. These groups are primarily run by volunteers in local communities, giving up their time and using their skills and compassion to make a difference. This short chapter contains stories from some volunteers explaining why they give up their time to support others and how this supports others.

The role of many charities and support services in helping those who have acquired brain injuries is enormously important – some links to support are included at the end of this book.

Of course, not everyone that acquires a brain injury needs major support. Some people are able to make strong recoveries and live fairly unaffected by their injury. However, many of these people will still have had moments of receiving support. Whether it is speaking to a doctor or nurse in an emergency department, or having a reassuring voice of a friend to help with processing events – many of us have someone to be thankful for.

The work of carers and their undeniable dedication is truly inspiring. We owe them so much.

# John

**Volunteer, 2022**

*I had purchased a derelict house with the aim of doing it up, but have since ended up living in it.*

During the course of renovating the house, I became friends with two neighbours across the street from me. I had seen them many times walking along the street with the aid of a frame. It took them a long time to cover such a short distance, but my admiration grew as their speed and the distances they achieved increased.

It was a chance conversation with his wife in the street that started my journey being involve with a local Headway branch and its members.

About 12 months after getting involved, I was asked if I would go to the Calvert Trust with them, an outdoor adventure centre for disabled people. I was asked if I would go with them as a carer. I enjoyed the weekend adventure and met many people involved in the group.

During the weekend, I met one member who wanted her garden revamped. She showed me the plans and costings, and it was obvious to me that she was being taken advantage of.

During this period, my friend became very ill and sadly passed away six months later. I then stepped in to care for her husband.

Over time, I have also taken on more responsibility within the group and look forward to helping those with brain injuries overcome the daily challenges they meet.

# Georgia

**Volunteer, 2022**

*I am a volunteer for Headway and have been since October 2021.*

I am helping to provide the invaluable support that our members receive after acquiring some kind of brain injury.

I find this role very rewarding and I am able to provide companionship and friendship to a range of people with differing needs. I found Headway whilst looking for volunteering opportunities in the local area to gain some experiences with vulnerable people to help prepare me well for my hopeful career in occupational therapy.

What I enjoy most about the role is talking to members about their lives and getting to know them as individuals. I see the benefits that group meetups have for our members in lifting their moods and allowing them the time and space to talk to people with similar struggles.

The work Headway does is remarkable and I am honored to work alongside them. I see the dedication of all committee members and volunteers and am assured of their passion and determination to those with brain injuries. I am excited to continue being a part of this organisation.

Before beginning to volunteer for Headway I had a slight misconception of those with brain injury and I think it's important to know that you cannot tell to look at someone that they have a brain injury and that is important to raise awareness of what is often an invisible strength.

# 7

# LINKS TO SUPPORT

Unlike some injuries, brain injuries can be difficult to understand and each injury is unique. As such, there is no set way to recover from a brain injury and the support that survivors require may differ.

This book has not aimed to give medical advice, however, it will, before it concludes, provide some links to support below which are relevant to a range of brain injuries and related conditions.

This list is not exhaustive and other support may be available in your locality.

**Headway** – the UK wide brain injury association that aims to improve life after brain injury. The charity provides a range of services including an emergency assistance fund, a brain injury identity card scheme and a directory of approved residential homes and rehabilitation units that specialise in ABI. The charity has a network of groups and branches across the UK that can provide a wide range of support in their local area.

Website: www.headway.org.uk
Helpline: 0808 800 2244

**Stroke Association** – a charity supporting people to rebuild their lives after they have had a stroke. The charity offers a range of support services, such as emotional and communication support, as well as important information. Stroke Association also completes research to help improve treatments and rehabilitation. The charity has a network of support services online and in local communities, which can be found on their website.

Website: www.stroke.org.uk
Helpline: 0303 3033 100

**The Brain Tumour Charity** – a charity dedicated to raising awareness of and funding research into brain tumours. The charity also campaigns for change and offers a range of support services for people affected by brain tumours.

Website: ww.thebraintumourcharity.org
Helpline: 0808 800 0004


**The Children's Trust** – a UK charity for children with brain injuries. The Trust has a residential rehabilitation centre in Tadworth, and also has its own school which provides a unique setting for children and young people with a wide range of special needs. The charity also offers a therapeutic support services to children anywhere in the UK and an information service to provide families with free support and advice.

Website: www.thechildrenstrust.org.uk
Switchboard: 01737 365 000


**Child Brain Injury Trust** – a charity supporting families and professionals working with children and young people with information about brain injuries. The Trust runs regular events, maintains and directory of support services, operates a local referral service and provides a Brain Injury Information Card service.

Website: ww.childbraininjurytrust.org.uk
Enquiries: 01869 341075

**Brain Injury Matters** - a Northern Ireland based charity which aims to support, promote and empower those affected by ABI. The charity delivers a number of programmes and initiatives to help those affected by brain injuries to become more independent, achieve their goals and adjust to life with brain injury.

Website: braininjurymatters.org.uk
Phone: 028 90 705 125

**Brain & Spine Foundation** – a UK wide charity providing information and support for over 470 neurological disorders. The Foundation provides a confidential helpline, a series of publications and events for patients, carers and healthcare professionals, as well as multiple online support groups.

Website: www.brainandspine.org.uk
Helpline: 0808 808 1000


**Carers UK** – a charity which provides expert advice, information and support through a telephone advice and support service. The charity also connects carers in local communities, works with local authorities to improve services for carers and aims to give carers a greater voice through campaign work.

Website: www.carersuk.org
Helpline: 0808 808 7777


**Carers Trust** – a charity working to improve support services and recognition for carers
Samaritans. The Trust provides a range of information online, and works with a network of partners to provide support.

Website: carers.org
Phone: 0300 772 9600

**Samaritans:** a charity which aims to provide emotional support to anyone in distress, having a difficult time, or simply needing someone to talk to. Samaritans works to ensure there is always someone there for anyone who needs someone. The charity provides a 24/7 listening service, and also provides support over email and other forms of communication.

Website: www.samaritans.org
Phone: 116 123

# 8

# CONCLUSION

*Brain injuries can be truly life-changing for both those who sustain them and the people around them.*

The injuries themselves, and the impacts that can follow are often incredibly difficult, painful and exhausting to experience, as the stories and themes in this book have explored. From simple trips and falls, to sports accidents and road traffic collisions, the stories have also shown how quickly lives can change, and how these injuries could happen to anyone.

While injuries are generally a negative topic, many of those who shared their stories for this book talked about feeling lucky, and some even about celebrating their injuries and how far they have come since.

Despite wishing to avoid them, traumatic injuries can have significant power in changing perspectives. Being able to find the positives in the apparent negatives, can take considerable effort and great perseverance.

In the course of interviewing survivors, I was continually inspired by their courage, both to open up about their stories, and in many cases how they have approached their recovery so positively. Whether you have experienced an injury yourself, support someone who has, or have been interested in learning about some real stories of brain injuries, I hope you have been inspired by reading the stories in this book.

This book started with the concept that you should never judge a book, nor a person, by their cover, and this is also how it now ends. It can be difficult, if not impossible to know what a person is going through at any one time, and arguably we shouldn't judge without knowing their full story.

As a form of hidden disability for many people, it is especially important that awareness is raised of brain injuries, some of their impacts, and how people can access support. This book has primarily aimed to give a voice to survivors and raise awareness of brain injuries as hidden disabilities – I hope that this book has provided some useful insights in this respect.

Though this book concludes here, the journeys faced by brain injury survivors, families and carers continue.

These journeys can be challenging and uncertain, but can be greatly aided by the support of others. Organisations across the country provide vital support for their members, though often rely on the work of committed volunteers and donations from the general public. Proceeds from this book will support some of these important causes, while further causes which can be accessed and supported have been highlighted in the Links to Support section of this book.

As well as the day-to-day challenges after sustaining a brain injury, many people will face the challenges of their injury not being recognised or understood. Both brain injuries, and misconceptions about them are common. The more people that learn even a small amount about brain injuries, the greater the potential for people's journeys to be that little bit easier – with this also being true for a range of other invisible or largely hidden disabilities. If you found this book insightful, please consider sharing it widely in order to increase awareness, understanding and respect.

Together, we can make a hugely positive impact to the lives of brain injury survivors, present and future.

**9**

# ACKNOWLEDGMENTS

This book wouldn't have been possible without the strength and courage of those who have shared their stories. The sharing of these stories is hugely important, though can often be difficult and bring back memories of emotional pain and physical trauma. To everyone who shared their story in the creation of this book, and to everyone else who bravely stands up to tell their story or aids others to do so, thank you.

I'd also like to extend a thank you to all of the volunteers at Bay Buddies and elsewhere for all that they do to support those who have sustained brain injuries, and specifically Janet, John and Angela who have played a big role in making this publication possible. If you're reading this, I also want to thank you - yes, you. Thank you for seeking to find out more about ABI and the stories of just some of those who are affected.

To Ben and the team at Lockstep Media that have sponsored the first edition of this book, and to David at Revo Creative for your cover design, a great big thank you. Thanks to your commitments and the purchases of everyone reading this, current and future brain injury survivors will continue to receive the support of a number of local groups, with 100% of revenues from this edition going to related charitable causes and community groups.

Thank you to Calum for the key learnings from our first book and your continued support.

I also owe significant thanks to a range of people who have offered support, listened and just been there when I've needed them in the time since my own injury. While I consider myself very lucky, working through my continued recovery has not been limited in its challenges, even for a relatively mild injury. To all those who have stuck by me and helped in ways big and small, a huge thank you.

Special thanks to my family, the OWT and County teams, Tom, Isaac and the many other friends and colleagues that have been so supportive. Your support means more than you know.

Nathan

# ABOUT THE AUTHOR

Nathan Shoesmith is an award-winning social entrepreneur and young leader, currently studying Management, Politics and International Relations at Lancaster University in the North West of England. Sustaining a brain injury himself in 2020, Nathan's own story was included earlier in this book.

Nathan's first book, '2020 As It Happened', was published in 2021, with Nathan having spent much of the pandemic as a journalist interviewing key politicians and health officials leading the fightback against COVID-19.

Nathan has raised awareness and over £12,000 for a variety of important charitable causes since 2014 and donated his time to write this publication. In recognition of efforts to increase access to understandable knowledge and inspire future generations, Nathan received the Diana Award in 2021, the highest accolade a young person can be awarded for social action or humanitarian efforts.